— RAVING R

"Matt is without a doubt 'The Powerful Promoter!' If you want to quickly increase your revenues and line your pockets with money again and again, he's definitely a Must read, Must hear, and Must see!"
—MIKE LITMAN, #1 International best-selling author of *Conversations with Millionaires* (New York, NY)

"Matt Bacak is one of the smartest marketers alive, but who cares, right? What matters to you is that he's a consummate teacher. He will not blow your mind with complex ideas – he'll just hold your hand and show you how to make a wad of cash."
—MARK JOYNER, #1 Bestselling Author of *Integration Marketing*

"You really need to call him Dr. Matt Bacak because he has a PHD in Affiliate and JV Marketing. I don't know anyone that knows more about Affiliates and JV's other then Matt."
—BILL GLAZER, #1 Bestselling Book author of *Outrageous Advertising*

"There is only 1 marketer that I have personally hired to consult me. I paid him $1,000 for a 1 hour consultation. The consultation happened in December, and from that 1 hour call I directly made over $250k."
—RUSSELL BRUNSON, Now Clickfunnels

HOW TO WRITE
EMAILS
THAT
SELL

HOW TO WRITE
EMAILS
THAT
SELL

SECRETS FROM THE
MOST PROFITABLE
EMAILS EVER WRITTEN

MATT BACAK

LEGAL STUFF

Income Disclaimer:

This document contains business strategies, marketing methods and other business advice that, regardless of my own results and experience, may not produce the same results (or any results) for you. I make absolutely no guarantee expressed or implied that by following the advice below you will make any money or improve current profits, as there are several factors and variables that come into play regarding any given business. Primarily, results will depend on the nature of the product or business model, the conditions of the marketplace, the experience of the individual, and situations and elements that are beyond your control. As with any business endeavor, you assume all risk related to investment and money based on your own discretion and at your own potential expense. Your results may vary. Success in ANY online endeavor is a result of hard work, time and a variety of other factors. No express or implied guarantees of income or spillover are made when reviewing the material provided.

Liability Disclaimer:

By reading this document, you assume all risks associated with using the advice given below, with a full understanding that you, solely, are responsible for anything that may occur as a result of putting this information into action in any way, and regardless of your interpretation of the advice. You further agree that my company cannot be held responsible in any way for the success or failure of your business as a result of the information presented below. It is your responsibility to conduct your own due diligence regarding the safe and successful operation of your business if you intend to apply any of our information in any way to your business operations.

Terms of Use:

You are given a non-transferable, "personal use" license to this product. You may not distribute it or share it with other individuals. There are no resale rights or private label rights granted when purchasing this document. In other words it's for your own personal use only.

Book Design by Kory Kirby
SET IN MINION PRO

CONTENTS

DEDICATION

I WOULD LIKE TO DEDICATE THIS BOOK TO ALL MY family, mentors, and amazing customers.

First, Mom and Dad.

Without you, this would never be.

Thank God... I was your fastest swimmer.

My wife, without you by my side, I'd never be where I am today.

Thank you for all the sacrifices you made to get us this far. Thank you for believing in me. I'll never forget the moment you looked at me and said, "You are a genius."

To my kids, you are nothing short of amazing.

I've been teaching you copy since the day you were born because it's so magical. May you use it wisely in all your future endeavors.

To Grandpa Grimm, thanks for being my first mentor. Giving me dreams and inspiration. Your words ring in my ears.

Ted Nicholas. Thank you for introducing me to copywriting. May you be celebrating in heaven.

Anyone that has ever written a direct response copy book, thank you.

My shelves are full of your works. I devour your teachings and more importantly apply them in life and business.

To all my amazing customers, clients, and members, without you and your actions this book would never been created.

I thank all of you.

Love you all.

—*MATT BACAK*

INTRODUCTION

HI.

My name is Matt Bacak.

I've been making millions from just sending emails for a very, very long time.

Many friends think I'm a master at it.

So am I a master, no. I'm a tester.

I can say without a shadow of a doubt, I'm probably one of the most prolific email split-testers that ever lived, much less, created a book like this.

I test to check if the self-appointed gurus are correct or just pulling stuff out of their butt.

Many times, I discover they are wrong and don't even know it because most of them are too lazy to set up a test that could instantly impact their results.

In case you are wondering, I've done over 8,000 tests in many different markets to many different email lists. So, what I'm sharing in this book, is not theory, it works.

I jokingly tell people that data is my religion.

Inside this book, you will discover what is not just tested, but proven to work.

Before you begin reading, let me tell you something I have learned over the years.

It's NOT the product, It's NOT where or how you advertise And It's NOT your price.

Nothing else is as important as writing an attention-grabbing, click-getting email.

That's where it all starts from.

Your email either pulls prospects and customers in or it pushes them away.

If your email doesn't do the job – nothing else matters.

The BOTTOM LINE:

It is all about RIGHT NOW.

It's about inspiring consumers to action the moment they're reading your email copy...

So, I challenge you.

Read this.

Then...

Apply it.

Today.

—*MATT BACAK*

CHAPTER #1

THE GREATEST EMAIL
WRITING SECRET
IN THE WORLD

THE NUMBER ONE REASON WHY YOU FIND email writing difficult is because you have not yet discovered…

The Greatest Email Writing Secret In The World.

Sounds overhyped, I know.

Yet, what I'm about to share with you is 100% true.

It's also easier than you ever dreamed possible.

Okay, that's two unbelievable promises to you in a row.

I just ask that you give me 30 seconds to explain why it's all true because it'll change the way you write emails for the rest of your career.

When you are armed with this secret, email writing requires very little creativity or original thought.

Email writing becomes simplified so much that your emails practically write themselves.

It works for you if you're writing emails for your own products, services, or coaching program.

It works for you if you're writing emails to promote affiliate offers.

So, without further ado, here's the secret…

> **Transfer the most powerful elements from the funnel sales page or VSL you're promoting into your emails.**

You see, most of your work is knowing how to select the right elements, such as particular sales copy and proof elements, from the actual funnel sales page you are promoting.

That's why you must know how to select the most

emotionally-charged elements from funnel pages, rework them if you must, and finally place them into a proven email structure.

Before we get into email structures (I'm going to show you how to write many email types), let's cover very quickly how to select these emotionally-charged elements.

There are 6 ways to cherry pick the most powerful elements for your emails.

Here's the first way…

> **1. Find <u>the most unique proof element</u> on the funnel page <u>that gives you an emotional gut punch</u>... and use it as the overall angle of your email.**

Sometimes this is an unusual proof element your list hasn't seen before.

For example, if you see a screenshot of results that beats the pants off the proof screenshots you've seen on other funnel pages, then you should consider using it in your email.

Let me give you a quick example.

Let's say that the funnel page you're promoting is for a product on Listbuilding.

You see a screenshot of 3,000 leads in one day.

It's not often you see a proof element with that much force.

So, now you take this information and feature it in your email.

Just watch out for this trap.

Sometimes you will see huge exciting claims without a lick of proof to back them up.

You shouldn't be promoting these types of funnel sales pages at all to your list because they are unsubstantiated.

Not only are we talking about possible legal repercussions (this is not legal advice, only common sense), but your subscribers won't believe the promise anyway.

Therefore, they won't buy.

That's why I say to look for the proof elements themselves, not the big promises.

Sure, you can use the copy angle built into the promise that the proof supports if the proof is there, but never use a huge promise that has no proof.

Another point on this…

Make sure the proof element has equal power as the promise.

If you're an affiliate and the product seller claims 3,000 leads in one day, yet shows screenshots of 500 leads in one day, then that proof does not equal the promise in terms of power.

If you're the product seller and you spot this type of disconnect on your funnel sales page, then tweak it so that your promises and proof elements have equal power.

Maybe that means "turning down the volume" of your promise.

Maybe that means finding a more exciting proof element and tying it to a promise of equal power.

Here's a second way to find the content of your email within the funnel sales page you're promoting…

2. Try to find how the product delivers an exciting result without usual restrictions.

Here's what I mean.

For example, if the sales page makes a promise of making $300 to $500 a day without having to do what you usually would have to do to make that kind of money, then this may be a great choice for email content.

In other words, look for evidence of a new way to get an exciting result.

Your subscribers are always looking for a fresh new way to fulfill their desires.

Usually, new ways of getting the same result they've always wanted involves overcoming previous restrictions of what you usually have to do to get that result.

Look for words like "without" on the funnel sales page you're promoting.

For instance, "How I Make $300 to $500 Per Day Without USUAL RESTRICTIONS."

The third way to select content for your email is by…

3. Looking for <u>a special discount</u> and <u>the reason</u> for the price slash.

Sift through the funnel sales page you're about to promote and try to find mention of a special deal such as a temporary price slash.

Also, look for their reason why they're slashing the price for this limited time period.

Both the price slash and the reason why the price has been slashed for a limited time become the main content of your email.

For example, let's say it's July 4th and an American product seller is offering an Independence Day Special Deal.

This becomes the overall content of your email.

Another example...

The product seller is offering 10% off for first time buyers.

10% off is the price slash and the reason for it is because the seller is trying to convert first time buyers into long-term customers.

This becomes the overall content of your email.

The fourth way is by...

4. Seeking out the <u>most unusual element</u> on the funnel sales page <u>in general</u>.

For example, maybe the funnel sales page you're promoting has a conditional guarantee.

Maybe it states that the customer will get $100 out of the seller's pocket if the product doesn't produce specific results.

You don't see this type of guarantee often, and that's why it's powerful.

So, it becomes the overall content and angle of your email.

The fifth way is by trying to...

5. Dig out <u>an element of urgency</u> on the funnel sales page.

This can be either unit based scarcity or time based scarcity.

If the funnel sales page says the product will only be available until a certain date, then you can use that information as the overall angle of your email.

If the funnel sales page says there are only a certain amount of units available, then you can use that information as the overall angle of your email.

If the funnel sales page has a countdown timer, then you can use that as the overall angle of your email.

The sixth and final way is by using your gut feeling to…

6. Cherry pick any element on the funnel sales page that gives you personally a big emotional reaction.

This isn't something that can be taught.

As you grow as an email writer, you start to develop a sort of intuition about these things.

You know from past experience what funnel sales page elements have converted well for you when used as overall email angles.

Also, you know what elements will cause an emotional

response in your subscribers based on what they have and haven't seen before.

Typically, the most unique and unusual elements convert the most clicks into sales and commissions because they build the most curiosity and desire in your subscribers.

Another reason for this is because an element may work well during one time period, but as these same elements are used over and over, they lose their emotional force.

So, it often takes unusual elements to get an emotional gut punch reaction out of your subscriber.

And, as everyone knows, subscribers buy things solely because of the emotional responses that your emails and funnel sales page copy stirs up in them.

Your email's overall job is to pre-sell by building desire for the promised results of the product or service before your subscribers even click through.

CHAPTER #2

5 EMAIL TYPES USED BY EMAIL WRITING MASTERS

THERE ARE POTENTIALLY LIMITLESS TYPES OF email structures that can work.

The most important part of an email isn't the structure at all.

It's what we talked about in Chapter 1, the content of the email.

However, you can more skillfully deliver that highly emotional content within the framework of proven email types.

This isn't to say you should be scared to invent your own frameworks.

Typically, any framework used on a sales page can be used as an email framework.

What exactly do I mean by framework?

Every email type imaginable has its own identifiable framework and can be replicated.

It's the overall structure of an email.

A good analogy would be to think of frameworks as containers that hold your emotional content that you have cherry picked from the funnel sales page you're promoting.

Therefore, in this section I'm going to share with you various frameworks that have been tested and proven to work time and time again.

I just want you to remember that great emails mainly write themselves once you hone your ability to cherry pick the hardest-hitting emotional elements off a funnel sales page and put it in your email.

What I'm saying is...

Don't get too caught up in frameworks because frameworks themselves can't sell anything well without having transferred the right elements into them.

Without cherry picking the most unique and hard-hitting elements, you end up with average results.

A true email writing master can double or triple the sales and commissions of an average email writer almost solely based on the ability to select the perfect funnel sales page elements for emails.

So, use these email types as a crutch until you feel comfortable creating your own from your selected emotional elements.

Make sense?

Good.

In truth, you need nothing more than these 5 email types and you'll be armed to the teeth with all the frameworks you need for the rest of your career.

That's not to say you shouldn't experiment with your own frameworks, because these 5 email types can be beaten by creative frameworks that themselves are new and unusual, for the same reasons that new and unusual content sets off a strong emotional reaction in your subscribers.

Just know that these 5 email types are tested and proven to work and are varied enough to create "containers" for the unique emotional elements you mine from funnel sales pages.

Let's get into the 5 proven email types of master email writers.

CHAPTER #3

IMPRESSIVE UNUSUAL RESULT EMAIL

THIS IS THE MOST BASIC EMAIL TYPE THAT YOU can quickly and easily use to amp up your sales and commissions.

It's also the most straightforward.

Its structure is as follows:

- SUBJECT: IMPRESSIVE UNUSUAL RESULT
- GREETING
- IMPRESSIVE UNUSUAL RESULT
- UNIQUENESS
- WHY IT'S EASY
- CALL TO ACTION
- LINK
- SIGNATURE

Example 1:

SUBJECT: 3,987 Leads in 1 Day

I wanted to give you a heads up about the results SELLER is getting with PRODUCT NAME.

SELLER is pulling in as many as 3,987 per day with this.

SELLER is USING NEW METHOD THAT YOUR SUBSCRIBERS HAVEN'T SEEN BEFORE.

It's only taking him X AMOUNT OF TIME OR EFFORT every time he uses NEW METHOD.

To get PRODUCT NAME working for you in your business, go here:

LINK

Talk soon,

YOUR NAME

Example 2:

SUBJECT: 1 Blog Post Brought In 1,919 New Customers in 1 Month

I just found a method that blew me away (and nothing impresses me much these days).

SELLER wrote 1 blog post using his NAME OF UNIQUE METHOD to bring in 1,919 new customers in 1 month.

Truth be told, up until today I thought blogging was dead, but SELLER'S UNIQUE METHOD showed me something I've never thought about before.

The crazy part?

It took SELLER 2 hours to write this new type of blog post, then he turned around and spent another 2 hours DOING SOMETHING EASY.

I suggest you go check it out for yourself now:

LINK

Talk soon,

YOUR NAME

Example 3:

SUBJECT: From 0 to 172,091 Free Website Visitors in 3 Months

This may be hard for you to believe.

I hardly believed it myself until I saw what SELLER was actually doing.

SELLER accidentally discovered how to take his new website from 0 to 172,091 free website visitors over the past 3 months.

Now he's sharing it with the world.

It's different from anything else you've seen before because of SELLER'S UNIQUE METHOD.

What's more?

SELLER made one small tweak and that's all it took to slam server crashing traffic to his site without spending a nickel on ads.

You've got to see this.

Grab yourself a copy of NAME OF PRODUCT here:

LINK

Talk soon,

YOUR NAME

CHAPTER #4

IMPRESSIVE UNUSUAL RESULT WITHOUT USUAL RESTRICTION EMAIL

THIS FRAMEWORK IS EXACTLY LIKE THE FIRST with one addition.

It highlights the fact that the product gets the desired result without usual restrictions.

As discussed in Chapter 1, you can often dig out this information from the funnel sales page you're about to promote.

Successful product sellers know this tactic well (even if it's just instinctually), so you'll find it in many successful funnel sales pages.

Pointing out existing results without usual restrictions works so well because it teases a fresh new mechanism that gets the desired result for you.

And, in highly-evolved niches such as IM, new product launches are often a battle of new mechanisms.

If these funnel sales pages don't outright tell you about a new mechanism that gets the desired result or teases a new mechanism that gets the desired result, then they often bomb.

The only time when a new mechanism isn't needed is when results are so incredible that such a hard-hitting and unusual proof element completely emotionally overwhelms a prospect to the point of purchase.

A mechanism is like a light switch.

It's the device that you flick on to provide light in your home.

You use the mechanism to get the desired result, light in your home.

So, mechanisms are just new ways to get the same old desired result your subscribers want.

Before electricity, the mechanism that provided light was a candlestick.

If you were selling the promise "puts light in your home" way back in the day, you would sell the mechanism as a candlestick.

If you were selling the promise "puts light in your home" during the time electricity was invented, you would sell the mechanism as a light switch.

Make sense?

If you want to truly be a master of marketing in general, not just email writing, then you must learn to understand how almost every product launch is nothing more than a battle of new mechanisms that get the same desired result that the market already wants.

So, for this type of email, if you understand the battle of new mechanisms across any highly-evolved market, then you can feature those mechanisms in your email either outright by telling your subscribers what that new mechanism is or by teasing new mechanisms blindly.

When you're saying in your email that subscribers

can potentially get the desired result without usual restrictions you're really saying that they get the desired result without using old mechanisms.

And you're teasing a new mechanism (a new way, a new HOW) that gets the desired result.

That said, the subject of mechanisms is usually confusing to people, and it's sad because understanding what mechanisms are, how they work, and how product sellers are in a constant war of providing new mechanisms means you can dominate any highly-evolved niche.

If you don't understand this battle of mechanisms, on the other hand, then you can never become a master email writer.

This email type structure is as follows:

- SUBJECT: IMPRESSIVE UNUSUAL RESULT Without USUAL RESTRICTIONS
- GREETING
- IMPRESSIVE UNUSUAL RESULT
- WITHOUT USUAL RESTRICTIONS
- CALL TO ACTION
- LINK
- SIGNATURE

Example 1:

SUBJECT: Build a 17,981 Facebook Group Without USUAL RESTRICTION

I hope you're ready to see what I just saw.

Why?

Because my head is spinning with the possibilities.

My friend SELLER just built a 17,981 member Facebook Group.

He did it all without usual restriction.

If you use this NEW METHOD, then you'll never have to USUAL RESTRICTION again.

Get started building your Facebook Group with it by going here now:

LINK

Talk soon,

YOUR NAME

Example 2:

SUBJECT: 6 Figs in Commissions Without USUAL RESTRICTION

This will make you smile ear to ear like the Cheshire Cat.

Or at least grin a little.

I just used my NEW METHOD to do 6 figs in CB commissions...

Without USUAL RESTRICTION #1...

Without USUAL RESTRICTION #2...

Without USUAL RESTRICTION #3...

See what I did by going here now:

LINK

Talk soon,

YOUR NAME

Example 3:

SUBJECT: Facebook Post Went Viral Without USUAL RESTRICTION

I never knew you could make a Facebook post go viral with this one little trick.

You have to see this...

Over the past few months, SELLER has been getting his Facebook posts to go viral.

The result?

Hoades upon hordes of free traffic to his website every day.

And he's making these posts go viral without USUAL RESTRICTION.

Check it out here:

LINK

Talk soon,

YOUR NAME

CHAPTER #5

DISCOUNT WITH A
REASON WHY EMAIL

PERHAPS DISCOUNT WITH A REASON WHY EMAILS are the one of the easiest to write because they are straight forward, short, and sweet.

They are common and you've seen so many of them that you can probably already write one that pulls in a fair amount of sales or commissions.

However, most marketers manage to settle for fair sales instead of explosive sales because they forget to add a reason for the discount in their emails.

Always remember to tie a reason to your discount.

That being said, most marketers forget to put the

reason why for the discount on their own funnel sales page.

A discount without a reason can bring in a fair amount of sales in itself, but a discount with a reason for the discount can rocket sales.

So, don't come up with a reason why if there isn't one already.

Remember, masterful email writing has mostly to do with transferring selected powerful and unusual elements from funnel sales pages to your email copy.

The structure for this type of email is as follows.

- SUBJECT: DISCOUNT
- GREETING
- DISCOUNT
- REASON WHY
- CALL TO ACTION
- SIGNATURE

Example 1:

SUBJECT: 10% Off PRODUCT NAME

I wanted to share this with you before it's too late.

For 3 days only, SELLER is offering 10% off PRODUCT NAME.

You see, he comes from a military family.

He himself is an Iraq War veteran.

That's why he's chosen to celebrate Memorial Day for not 1 but 3 days in a row with this special discount.

Grab your copy here for 10% off before it's too late:

LINK

Talk soon,

YOUR NAME

Example 2:

SUBJECT: Early Bird Discount

If you're having a bad day, then this will brighten your day like a shining star.

That's because I just released PRODUCT NAME.

Get it now, along with my other subscribers only, for a steep Early Bird Discount.

This discount is only for you and my subscribers because I value you the most.

When I release PRODUCT NAME to the public in 48 hours from now, they will have to pay full price.

Go here and get in at the Early Bird Discount price:

LINK

Talk soon,

YOUR NAME

Example 3:

SUBJECT: 50% Off [2 Days Left]

When was the last time you've seen a special offer this generous?

You get 50% off PRODUCT NAME if you grab it within the next 2 days.

After that, it goes back to full price for good.

SELLER is giving you a 50% discount because REASON WHY.

Go here and get in at half off while you can here:

LINK

Talk soon,

YOUR NAME

CHAPTER #6

URGENCY EMAIL

OF COURSE, YOU ALWAYS ADD URGENCY BEFORE the call to action in every email when that element is available on the funnel sales page you're promoting.

However, there's a type of email that is all based around urgency from beginning to end.

They are perhaps the most powerful type of email (especially when there's less than 24 hours to act) and also the easiest to write because they are short and punchy.

The structure is as follows:

- SUBJECT: URGENCY
- GREETING

- URGENCY
- CALL TO ACTION
- SIGNATURE

Example 1:

SUBJECT: 1 Spot Left

Spots for **COACHING PROGRAM NAME** have been selling like hot cakes.

In fact, at the very moment I'm writing this email there is only 1 spot left.

Not 3.

Not 2.

1.

Just 1 spot.

And when the final spot is taken, doors will close forever.

Be fast and go here to claim the final spot:

LINK

Talk soon,

YOUR NAME

Example 2:

SUBJECT: 250 Copies Only

Heads up.

You'll want to get a copy of PRODUCT NAME before all 250 are gone.

SELLER has already sold over 150 copies and might only have a handful left right now.

Be fast.

Go here and grab your copy:

LINK

Talk soon,

YOUR NAME

Example 3:

SUBJECT: Closes in 4 Hours

Be fast.

Class registration for NAME OF PROGRAM closes in 4 hours from now.

This is your last chance to get in.

Enroll here now:

LINK

Talk soon,

YOUR NAME

CHAPTER #7

BENEFIT PILE-ON EMAIL

WHEN YOU HAVE NO SPECIAL DISCOUNT OR urgency to create an overall email angle, writing a Benefit Pile-On Email might be exactly what you need to intensify the desire of your subscribers for the product you're pitching.

This is different from the first 2 email types in that it focuses on shotgun blasting multiple promises, not just 1 promise or result.

The words "You will" or "You'll" become the tool of choice for writing Benefit Pile-On Emails.

The structure is as follows:

- SUBJECT: MOST POWERFUL BENEFIT

- GREETING
- BENEFIT PILE-ON
- CALL TO ACTION
- SIGNATURE

Example 1:

SUBJECT LINE: One Tweak, Huge Profit

I was planning on hoarding this little tweak and never sharing it with anyone.

But something tells me you could use it too.

When I show you this little tweak...

You'll BENEFIT 1...

You'll BENEFIT 2...

You'll BENEFIT 3...

You'll BENEFIT 4...

You'll BENEFIT 5...

Check it out here:

LINK

Talk soon,

YOUR NAME

Example 2:

SUBJECT: New Machine Adds 200 Subscribers To Your List Per Day

Machine... Software... AI...

I guess it's all the same, right?

Wrong.

This software/machine/AI actually works.

When you use SOFTWARE PRODUCT NAME...

You'll add up to 200 new subscribers to your list per day...

You'll do it all without forking over a single penny for traffic...

You'll leverage traffic sources that already exist to flood your squeeze page with new visitors...

You'll only install this software once, spend less than an hour per day fiddling with it, and it creates a steady flow of traffic to your site...

You'll get a piece of software that, unlike most, truly does the hard work for you...

Go here and grab your copy of NAME OF SOFTWARE now:

LINK

Talk soon,

YOUR NAME

Example 3:

SUBJECT: 16,891 Website Visitors Stomped His Server

You know how gurus are always bragging about their launches?

About how their affiliates sent so much traffic that it crushed their server?

You and I both know that's nothing to really brag about.

Imagine getting 16,891 server smashing website visitors in less than 24 hours with 1 cent traffic.

That's exactly what SELLER did with the new technique he'll show you in PRODUCT NAME.

You'll pay only 1 cent per website visitor...

You'll send whole marching armies of traffic to your website minute by minute, hour by hour...

You'll never rely on affiliates for traffic again...

You'll never have to write another blog post again...

You'll never have to launch another product again...

Go here and see how powerful this is:

LINK

Talk soon,

YOUR NAME

CONCLUSION

IF YOU TAKE THE ADVICE IN THIS BOOK TO heart and apply it with every email you write, then you will, in a short time, become an email writing master.

You can use these tactics to write emails for your own products, services, and coaching programs.

You can offer an email writing service and use only these principles to charge $100 or more for every email you write.

It's also important to note that the 5 email types are useful only for strategically placing the most powerful sales page elements inside your emails.

If you want to write emails that truly build desire before your subscribers land on the funnel sales page you're promoting, then know that email writing mastery has mostly to do with careful selection of sales page elements.

In other words, masterful emails aren't written out of thin air.

They require little creativity, little original thought.

They are the type of emails that hit your subscribers in the gut with strong emotion.

Also, writing your emails this way makes them correspond perfectly to the funnel sales page you're promoting.

This is one of the master keys in itself, though it hasn't been talked about in this report because the feeling of continuity between email and funnel sales page is a natural byproduct of the way I've shown you to write masterful emails.

It provides a sales psychology similar to how presell pages work when running display traffic.

I'll leave you with this question to ask yourself as you're writing emails, "How can I find the most powerful funnel sales page elements for my emails that are unusual and unique enough to stir strong emotion in my subscribers?"

Ask yourself this question as you're mining elements to use in your emails because this is how email writing masters build desire in their subscribers so that they excitedly go to the promoted page and buy, buy, buy.

AN OPEN LETTER TO THE GRAMMAR AND SPELLING POLICE

DEAR GRAMMAR AND SPELLING POLICE,

If you find any errors, grammar or spelling wise, please email us your edits at mattbacak@gmail.com with the subject line "HTWE" and we will gladly make note of them for the updated version of the book and I'm very serious about that.

However, I'm also serious about this:

If it bothers you that I can't spell and my grammar sucks, then go look at your bank account and ask yourself, why doesn't my banker ask me how good I can spell when I cash checks at the bank.

My banker never asked me that. My banker just cares about the checks being cashed.

Heck, Kory who did the interior design of this book said, "I once cashed a check with my name spelled wrong on it. Still worked."

Do not let a few mistakes get in the way of your success. I hate to say this, but I have found that the perfectionists, the ones that write perfectly, tend to get in their own way of success. Please don't let that be you.

Please think, if this guy who can't even spell makes millions from writing emails, by God, I know I can do it too.

Also note, this "AIN'T" school.

In fact, writing direct response copy has nothing to do with the regular rules of writing.

A lot of people who do well in writing at school, struggle with copywriting because they just can't shake those rules, or the desire to find a better way of describing something.

I will admit I'm not the best writer in the world, but I sure do know how to sell.

That being said, if you want to make a lot of money with your emails...

Then find your true self and write in a friendly, conversational, rule-breaking style.

Hope you enjoyed the book.

—MATT BACAK

HOW TO CONTACT MATT BACAK

FIRST, THANK YOU FOR READING MY BOOK. For all inquiries about Coaching, Consulting, Speaking or Interviews please contact me at:

MattBacak@gmail.com

Email Marketing is a Revenue Engine You Simply Can't Ignore.

ABOUT THE AUTHOR

MATT BACAK IS THE FOUNDER OF THE EPC
Institute and a Award-Winning Email Marketer. He
started marketing online in 1997 and has been email
marketing since 1999. He put up my first opt-in page
in 2001. In 2003, he made his first million dollars
from email marketing. He has sent well over a bil-
lion emails in the last 18 years. At last count, he's
done over 8,000 email split test rounds. His lists
are growing by up-to 10,978 subscribers a DAY!
He has helped a number of clients target his spe-
cialty, opt-in email direct marketing systems. He
is not only a sought-after digital marketer but has
also marketed for some of the world's top experts
whose reputations would shrivel if their followers
ever found out someone else coached them on their
email marketing and his passion is helping people
like you make more money from email because email

marketing is one of the most powerful tools in your digital marketing repertoire.

Printed in Great Britain
by Amazon